BENNY HINN MINISTRIES PRESENTS

BIBLE FOODS *for* LIFE

CLARION CALL MARKETING

DALLAS, TEXAS

BIBLE FOODS FOR LIFE

Jacqueline Overpeck, Editor

© 2006 Clarion Call Marketing

Published by Clarion Call Marketing
P.O. Box 610010
Dallas, TX 75261

Scripture quotations, unless otherwise indicated, are taken from the *New King James Version*. Copyright © 1982 by Thomas Nelson, Inc. Used by permission. All rights reserved.

Scripture quotations marked KJV are taken from the *King James Version*.

Disclaimer: This booklet is intended as a reference volume only, not as a medical guide. The information provided is intended to help the reader make informed decisions about his or her health but is in no way intended as a substitute for any professional medical treatments.

ISBN 1-59574-067-8

Printed in the United States of America

First Edition 2006

10 9 8 7 6 5 4 3 2

Contents

FOREWORD

"For I will restore health to you and heal you of your wounds," says the LORD.

JEREMIAH 30:17

Promises regarding healing and health are found throughout the Bible. And without reservation, I believe that it is God's will for us to be well, to enjoy health and life in their fullness. God's will for us to walk in divine health and a right relationship with Him is emphasized in the New Testament. *"Beloved,"* reads 3 John 2, *"I wish above all things that thou mayest prosper and be in health, even as thy soul prospereth"* (KJV).

This prosperity of health comes as we give ourselves to the things of God's Spirit and use wisdom regarding the care of our physical body. It is vitally important that we observe the laws of nature and the guidelines offered by medical science. We must be careful not to abuse our body through improper nutrition, lack of rest, or exposure to undue stress.

Medical science can help us along the way. New breakthroughs are constantly being discovered that provide insight into good health. This includes information on lifestyle, diet, exercise, stress, environmental-related issues, mental health, and many other areas that relate to our total sense of well-being.

Never forget this important truth: The Spirit of God abides within you. Scripture tells us that we are His temple: *"Do you not know that your body is the temple of the Holy Spirit who is in you, whom you have from God?"* (1 Corinthians 6:19). It is our responsibility to be faithful to take good care of the physical body the Creator has given to us.

Who better to provide dietary insight than our wonderful Lord? *Bible Foods for Life* highlights nine foods full of nutritional value that are spoken of in God's Word. Throughout the rest of this booklet you will discover the phenomenal health benefits of some of the Bible's richest life-giving food resources, including:

1. Fish
2. Beans
3. Leeks, Onions, and Garlic
4. Water
5. Cucumber
6. Apples
7. Nuts

We've included a special recipe for each food for you to enjoy along with additional information on the health benefits of Ezekiel bread, tomatoes, and yogurt.

God is and has always been the Healer. He said, *"I am the LORD that healeth thee"* (Exodus 15:26, KJV). It is His will for you to live in divine health. Whatever you are facing today, the God of miracles is able to perfect all that concerns you (see Psalm 138:8). You can trust Him to restore your health and renew your youth (see Isaiah 40:31). My prayer is that you will walk in the fulfillment of Jeremiah 30:17: *"For I will restore health to you and heal you of your wounds,' says the LORD."*

Healing and health belong to you as God's dear child!

—BENNY HINN

FISH

These you may eat of all that are in the water: whatever in the water has fins and scales, whether in the seas or in the rivers—that you may eat.

LEVITICUS 11:9

FISH IN THE BIBLE

During Bible times, fishing was a major industry along the Jordan River and the Sea of Galilee. Jesus and the Jewish people ate a wide variety of fish due to the great availability of fresh seafood in Jerusalem's marketplace. At the time of Jesus, the average person would select meat only for special occasions. Meat would have been considered a main course set aside for times of festivity. Fish remained the diet staple because it was less expensive and easier to obtain.

Fishing was important in the life and ministry of Jesus. Prior to Jesus's calling several of His disciples, they were professional fishermen. This may be part of the reason that a number of Jesus's parables, miracles, and teachings concerned fish.

Twice Jesus fed multitudes of people with just a few fish. On one occasion, He took five loaves and two fish, blessed them, broke them, and gave them to His disciples to feed five thousand men, plus women and children in the crowd (see Matthew 14:16-21). Later, Jesus took seven loaves and "a few little fish" and gave thanks for them, broke them, and gave them to His disciples to feed four thousand men, besides the women and children (see Matthew 15:32-37). The "little fish" may have been sardines, a small fish of the herring family.[1] In both miracles, everyone was fed and there were even portions left over!

Health Benefits of Fish

Fish is an excellent source of healthy protein, and it's low in saturated fats. In addition to this, most fish are naturally low in calories and are rich in healthy oils, vitamins, and minerals.

Some people do not care to eat fish because of its

fishy taste and smell. But it's worth learning to eat fish, even if you don't eat it regularly at first. Fish, deemed clean in Leviticus 9, are an excellent source of omega-3 fatty acids, protein, potassium, vitamins, and minerals. Here are a few of the many superb health benefits to eating fish that Dr. Jordan Rubin cites:

- Thins the blood
- Protects arteries from damage
- Inhibits blood clots (antithrombotic)
- Reduces blood triglycerides
- Lowers LDL blood cholesterol
- Lowers blood pressure
- Reduces the risk of heart attack and stroke
- Eases symptoms of rheumatoid arthritis
- Reduces the risk of lupus
- Relieves migraine headaches
- Fights inflammation
- Helps regulate the immune system
- Inhibits cancer in animals (and possibly humans)
- Soothes bronchial asthma
- Combats early kidney disease[2]

According to some leading healthcare professionals, certain foods have been discovered to have a significant effect on mood, memory, and other mental functions. Fish, known as a brain food for its high selenium, may be one of them. Research in this area has led many nutritionists to believe that a lack of selenium can cause some people to suffer from depression, fatigue, and anxiety. Findings indicate that proper amounts of selenium improves mood significantly.

Vitamin B_{12}, a key immune system booster, is found in cold-water fish. Vitamin B_{12}, or cobalamin, may help prevent memory loss, impaired abstract thinking skills, and mental confusion. Making wise food choices, including fresh fish, can help overcome the effects of illness, including Alzheimer's disease, by helping to block aluminum toxicity.

IMPORTANCE OF FRESH FISH

Think there's something fishy about the mass sale of seafood around town? You're not the only one! Many healthcare professionals speak out about the importance of finding supermarkets that sell fresh fish, and they recommend buying Pacific salmon, sole, and tuna due to their low level of mercury. Mahi-mahi, trout, halibut, and grouper are also good choices.

It's important that the fish come from unpolluted, fresh pure waters. Fish from these locations are preferred: Alaska, Argentina, Chili, Iceland, and New Zealand.

Storing and cooking fish properly is also important to ensuring that your fish holds the highest nutritional benefits. In *Walking in Divine Health,* Dr. Don Colbert provides a checklist to help you purchase quality fish:

- Fresh fish must be shiny, bright, and bulging.
- If it smells fishy, don't buy it.
- If the scales are shiny, the fish is good.
- If your touch leaves an indentation in the flesh, don't buy it. The flesh should spring back.
- If the fish has not been kept on ice at 32 degrees, don't buy it. It is likely that it has already begun to spoil.[3]

Are there some fish to avoid? Yes, say "no thank you" to these: shark, swordfish (due to high mercury levels and pesticides), raw fish (due to tapeworms or other parasites), and shellfish.

How much fish should an individual eat? The American Heart Association recommends that the average adult have at least two servings of fish every week. Pregnant women should consult their doctor concerning fish to avoid.

Fish Recipe

Citrus Salmon

    1 lb. salmon steaks*

    ½ c. mayonnaise

    ½ c. olive oil

    ¼ c. citrus fruit juice

    1 pinch of lemon pepper

Mix citrus fruit juice, mayonnaise, and olive oil until well blended. Pour the mixture over the salmon. Cover and marinate in refrigerator for an hour. Drain. Place the salmon on a greased grill over medium coals. Grill for about 5 minutes on each side.

* You may substitute salmon for any firm-fleshed, thick,-sliced fish of your preference.

BEANS

*And Jacob gave Esau bread and stew of lentils; then he
ate and drank, arose, and went his way.*

GENESIS 25:34

BEANS IN THE BIBLE

In Bible times, beans, peas, and lentils, easily grown,
were used for a variety of dishes, including coarse
bread, known as Ezekiel bread. Due to their simplicity
of drying and storing, beans, peas, and lentils were
plentiful year-round.

Lentils, commonly consumed in Israel during biblical times, are actually one of the oldest cultivated plants.
Archaeological evidence indicated that they were cultivated in the Near East as early as 18,000 BC. Bible
scholars believe that many of the beans mentioned in
the Bible included broad beans such as the fava.

Throughout the Bible there seems to be a consistent message: Beans are a tremendous source of nutrition and health. Being so, they were a staple source of food during Bible times. The Word of God clearly illustrates their popularity in the lives of Esau and Daniel.

The story of Jacob and Esau is one of the most powerful stories in Genesis. We are told that Esau had been out in the field hunting all day and came home very hungry and was even feeling faint. Esau smelled a pot of soup cooking, and he said to his brother, Jacob, "Please feed me with that same red stew, for I am weary" (Genesis 25:30). Red stew is an ancient dish in the Middle East made of beans and lentils boiled in garlic—a wholesome, tasty meal. Jacob capitalized on his brother's hunger and bought Esau's birthright for that stew (see Genesis 25:31).

In the life of Daniel, we see that he had a good understanding of the nutritious value of beans. When offered the king's meat, Daniel refused. Instead, he asked for pulse (broad beans) and water (Daniel 1:12). Why? Daniel sought to keep his mind sharp, body strong, and remain on guard. He didn't want to let down his defenses by eating foods that might cause him to weaken in purpose (Daniel 1:15). Beans have an amazing ability to reduce the rise in blood sugar after meals, and allow a gradual more natural drop in blood sugar later on.

The book of Ezekiel also points to the body-strengthening benefits of beans used in bread. God said to Ezekiel, *"Also take for yourself wheat, barley, beans, lentils, millet, and spelt; put them into one vessel, and make bread of them for yourself"* (Ezekiel 4:9). You'll find more information about "Ezekiel Bread" in the Additional Healthy Foods section at the back of this booklet, along with a special recipe showing you how to make this biblical bread right in your own kitchen.

HEALTH BENEFITS OF BEANS

When considering your diet, place beans high on the list. Doing so may help you avoid a trip to the doctor's office. According to some doctors, many Americans rarely take in the amount of fiber their bodies need on a daily basis. Studies reveal that most people should be consuming at least double, in some cases, triple their current fiber intake.

Fiber is an all-around good addition to any diet. Beans, a healthy source of good fiber, can help improve your nutritional intake of this life-giving nutrient. In addition, eating beans has a positive effect on an individual's gastrointestinal tract, helps prevent type 2 diabetes, and lowers cholesterol.

According to the USDA, dried beans and peas are the mature forms of legumes such as kidney beans, pinto beans, lima beans, black-eyed peas, and lentils. These foods are excellent sources of plant protein and also provide other nutrients such as iron and zinc. Lentils have 7.5 percent protein, but they are deficient in the amino acids methionine and cysteine. They are very low in fat and contain high amounts of soluble fiber that help to lower cholesterol and control blood sugar. Lentils are similar to meats, poultry, and fish in their contribution of these nutrients. Many people consider dried beans and peas as vegetarian alternatives for meat. However, they are also excellent sources of dietary fiber and of nutrients such as foliate that are low in diets of many Americans.

Dr. Don Colbert has made a list of the marvelous health benefits of beans. Beans are high in vitamin C, an excellent antioxidant. One cup of cooked beans daily is recommended to help prevent heart disease and to provide:

- 6 to 7 grams of fiber
- Potassium, iron, and thiamine
- 12 grams of complex carbohydrates or starches
- 17.9 grams of protein[1]

Many healthcare professionals agree that beans—soybeans in particular—which contain genistein are a leading cancer-fighting food. They prevent cells from developing into malignancy and serve to block the blood supply to cancer cells. Some findings have indicated that this is considerably beneficial in the case of breast or ovarian cancer by blocking certain estrogen receptors.

Millions of Americans suffer from various forms of

stress and anxiety. Did you know that bean consumption may help calm mental and emotional imbalance? Nutritionists claim that beans might relieve those suffering with mental and emotional anxiety, in part due to the B vitamins they contain. B vitamins are key to sustaining the nervous system, brain function, and energy level. Nutritionists believe that beans can help relieve a multitude of other discomforting symptoms as well, such as fear, irritability, insomnia, high blood pressure, head and neck aches, stiff and tight muscles, dizziness, loss of appetite, stomach problems, constipation, ulcer, colitis, rapid heartbeat, and shallow breathing.

The U.S. Department of Agriculture states that because of beans' high nutrient content, consuming dried beans and peas is recommended for everyone, including people who also eat meat, poultry, and fish regularly.

Lentils are good in combination with other vegetables in soups, stews, and casseroles. Preparing dried beans is simple. Soak them in water overnight—twice the amount of water to beans. Discard the old water and add fresh water to cook. Doing so will eliminate much of the gas-causing effects of the beans.

Still looking for more reasons to add beans to your dinner menu? How about this: they help keep you fit by burning fat. They're high in protein and free from saturated fats. Doctors and nutrition experts both suggest they're a good weight-loss food. Beans naturally regulate blood-sugar levels and stabilize blood glucose. They suppress the appetite while increasing strength.

Other types of beans that are highly nutritious are lima beans, green peas, black-eyed peas, white beans, navy beans, black beans, and kidney beans. All of these beans are high in soluble fiber and high in protein, but low in the amino acids cysteine and methionine.[2]

Why eat beans? Besides the health benefits, they're economical. Overall, beans are one of the best food choices you can make.

BEANS RECIPE

Fassolatha
(Greek Bean Soup)

  2 c. dried navy beans
  ⅓ c. extra-virgin olive oil
  1 large mild onion, finely diced
  2 carrots, finely diced or sliced
  2 large cloves garlic, finely chopped
  2 stalks celery, with leaves, chopped
  tsp. pepper
  8-10 c. water
  1 can diced tomatoes
  1 tsp. sea salt
  ½ c. parsley, minced

Optional: 1 c. fresh spinach, sliced into paper thin ribbons

Soak beans overnight in twice the amount of water. Drain the beans and place them in fresh cold water in a large pot. Slowly bring to a boil and boil for 3 minutes. Drain, rinse, and set aside. In a big soup pot, sauté the onion, carrot, and garlic in the oil on low heat for 20–25 minutes, stirring occasionally, until the vegetables are golden. Stir in the celery and pepper. Add the beans, and then add 8 cups of water and stir. Bring to a boil. Reduce heat, cover, and simmer for 1 hour, until the beans are soft but not falling apart. Sprinkle the tomatoes with the sea salt, and let sit for 15 minutes, while soup continues cooking. Stir in the tomatoes (and spinach, if desired), and let simmer another 10 minutes. To serve, ladle into bowls and garnish with parsley. Serves 6.

LEEKS, ONIONS, AND GARLIC

We remember the fish which we ate freely in Egypt, the cucumbers, the melons, the leeks, the onions, and the garlic.

NUMBERS 11:5

LEEKS, ONIONS, AND GARLIC IN THE BIBLE

Leeks, onions, and garlic have been valued for their flavor as well as for their herbal remedies for thousands of years. Onions are one of the first foods mentioned in written text in general.

Although these foods can leave a pungent odor and flavor, people of Bible days understood their benefits. Egyptian laborers ate leeks, onions, and garlic to increase their stamina and maximize endurance as they constructed Khufu's pyramid. Onions were thought to bring great energy for hard manual labor. Garlic was most commonly enjoyed as a component of Lebanese dishes; it also became a staple food of the Israelites in Egypt (see Numbers 5).

Leeks are appreciated for their versatility in cooking. They are greatly appreciated in traditional meals of the Middle East. The leek's flavor is mild and sweeter to taste in comparison to its stronger cousins, onions and garlic. Garlic is still grown in Egypt today, however Syrian garlic is favored. One common use in Lebanon is garlic sauce on salads.

HEALTH BENEFITS OF
LEEKS, ONIONS, AND GARLIC

Garlic, onions, and leeks are members of the lily family and close in relation. Research shows that several dozen or more anticancer compounds are present in these life-giving foods. Both garlic and onions contain allium compounds (diallyl sulfides). Healthcare professionals claim that these important compounds help increase the activity of cancer-fighting immune cells.

Other benefits provided by leeks, onions, and garlic are numerous. Some have used onions as an antiseptic and a pain reliever. Many leading physicians suggest that onions may possess various antibiotic properties that fight against bacteria, fungi, and parasites. It's also good to note that onions provide flavonoids, a group of nutrients found in vegetables which are essential for processing vitamin C and needed to maintain capillary walls, or antioxidants that quench free-radical reactions. The juicy peel is a good place to find a high number of healthy flavonoids.

Garlic is hailed as being greatly beneficial by top healthcare professionals all over the world. According to Dr. Don Colbert, garlic has numerous health benefits, including benefits to the immune system.

Japanese scientists have distilled an antibiotic medication called kyolic from raw garlic. Kyolic has also been used to fight influenza—including a severe outbreak in Moscow in the 1950s—as well as to ward off pneumonia, whooping cough, and various intestinal disorders. Researchers are speculating that one of the reasons garlic is such an effective medicine is because it boosts the body's natural immunity. Studies have shown that garlic appears to help slow blood coagulation, and it has antioxidant properties.[1]

Reports suggest that garlic may also help with poor circulation. Adding garlic to your recipes is a good way to relieve high blood pressure and possibly dilate or help open the arteries and aid the cardiovascular system. Nutritionists claim that not only can garlic help prevent cancer, but it also directly fights the disease and can stimulate the body's defense mechanisms.

Reese Dubin, author of *Miracle Food Cures from the Bible,* explains that garlic has been shown to fight bacteria, strengthen the immune system, raise the good (HDL) cholesterol, and fight cancer. Along with this, he created a list of the requirements garlic seems to fulfill as a therapeutic agent to reduce blood pressure:

1. It is absolutely safe.
2. There are no bad after-effects; no limit to dosage has been found.
3. Blood pressure is reduced gradually without a

sudden drop that could shock the system.

4. It will not interfere with any other medication you may be taking, under a doctor's care.

5. In almost every case tested, it has relieved weakness, dizziness, headaches, ringing ears, chest pain, and annoying gas pains.

6. Good results may be obtained regardless of age or condition.

7. It is easy to take in odor-free tablet form.[2]

If you are deciding whether or not to consume garlic based upon the odor, make the choice to add this life-giving food to your regular diet. One clove daily is a good, healthy start. Or you may choose to take dried garlic extract in capsules. It's much better to distance yourself from sickness than to be concerned with garlic distancing people from you.

Leeks, Onions, and Garlic Recipe

Creamy Zucchini and Garlic

   3 medium zucchini squash, grated
   3 medium yellow squash, grated
   1 large onion, finely chopped
   2-3 leeks, finely chopped
   6 garlic cloves, minced
   2½ tbsp. butter
   1 tsp. thyme leaves, chopped
   2½ tbsp. sour cream
   fresh ground pepper

Melt butter in a skillet. Add the minced garlic, onions, and leeks, and sauté over low heat for a short time. Add all grated squash and thyme. Cook, stirring frequently until the squash is tender. Remove from heat and top with sour cream and fresh ground pepper.

WATER

For the LORD your God is bringing you into a good land, a land of brooks of water, of fountains and springs, that flow out of valleys and hills.

DEUTERONOMY 8:7

WATER IN THE BIBLE

The importance of water is emphasized throughout the Word of God. In fact, it's mentioned over six hundred times in the New King James Version. Its value as a prized possession is well understood down through generations and across lands, both ancient and present day. The land of the Bible, Israel, is no exception in treasuring the immense worth of this natural resource.

Ancient water wells have been dug deep throughout Israel and the world. A great common denominator of all life is our need for water. Proper hydration is the key building block to good health. K. C. Craichy, author of *Super Health: 7 Golden Keys to Unlock Lifelong Vitality,* put it this way:

> Water is our life-support system, the blood that runs through our veins, the blue arteries of the earth. In some ways, it is the prerequisite of all other human rights, because it is the ultimate substance that enables us to lead a healthy life...not to mention one of dignity and balance. Water is also the most beautiful of all molecular compounds and the most useful as well. In the biblical account of creation, we learn that *"the Spirit of God was hovering over the face of the waters"* (Genesis 1:2). The foundation of the entire living world is built on the many unique properties of water—the ultimate biological solvent.[1]

The Old Testament makes numerous references to water, including the memorable story of the Israelites in exile from Egypt and how God used Moses and his rod to supernaturally bring forth water from a rock. God's great promise for the children of Israel was to bring them into a *"good land, a land of brooks of water, of fountains, and springs, that flow out of valleys and hills"* (Deuteronomy 8:7).

And the LORD said to Moses, "Go on before the people, and take with you some of the elders of Israel. Also take in your hand your rod with which you struck the river, and go. Behold, I will stand before you there on the rock in Horeb; and you shall strike the rock, and water will come out of it, that the people may drink." (Exodus 17:5-6)

Then the LORD spoke to Moses, saying, "Take the rod; you and your brother Aaron gather the congregation together. Speak to the rock before their eyes, and it will yield its water; thus you shall bring water for them out of the rock, and give drink to the congregation and their animals." (Numbers 20:7-8)

The New Testament also contains a wealth of wisdom relating to water and its life-nourishing qualities, both physically and figuratively. Consider the spiritual lesson Jesus shared with the Samaritan woman during their most memorable conversation at the well.

Jesus asked her for a drink. She was taken aback that a Jewish man would speak with her. Nonetheless, she met his request and provided him with water. To that, Jesus said, *"If you knew the gift of God, and who it is who says to you, 'Give Me a drink,' you would have asked Him, and He would have given you living water"* (John 4:10). Just like the Samaritan woman at the well, we can look to Jesus to quench our thirst for living water. Only He can grant salvation and eternal life with God, whereby we never thirst again.

Health Benefits of Water

The human body instinctively yearns for wholesome water. Drinking enough water to satisfy your body is a first basic step to enhance your life and increase your lifespan. If you were to ask a healthcare professional, "What is the most important element of life, and how can I utilize that element to remain healthy?" He or she would most likely answer, "Water, and the more you drink the better." Why? Water transports nutrients to the cells.

People can survive for months without food but only a few days without water. The body uses water for digestion, absorption, circulation, transporting nutrients, building tissues, carrying away waste, and maintaining body temperature.

Physicians caution that many people do not take in near the amount of water their body needs each day. K. C. Craichy tells us:

> Part of the reason is that thirst is often tied to a sensation, such as dry mouth, or camouflaged behind a number of other bodily perceptions, such as hunger or fatigue. Consequently, by the time we actually experience the sensation of thirst, it's often too late. We're *already* acutely dehydrated, and it is this state of dehydration that can lead to all sorts of negative physical and mental symptoms, and even death itself. A tiny deficiency of water in the body is more than enough to cause our cells to begin to malfunc-

tion, catalyzing the downward spiral of most degen-
erative diseases. [2]

Here are some amazing facts about water, given by
Dr. Don Colbert in his stirring book *What You Don't
Know May Be Killing You!:*

- Your body is about 60 percent water.
- Your muscles are about 75 percent water.
- Your brain is about 75 percent water.
- Your blood is approximately 82 percent water.
- Your bones are approximately 25 percent water. [3]

The health benefits of water are numerous. The
best health decision you can make today is to start
drinking more water. Proper water intake is imperative
to your overall well-being. Accept no substitutes for
pure, cold, life-giving water.

If you're having trouble drinking the recommended
eight glasses a day, try adding a spritz of lemon or lime
juice (or thoroughly washed sliced citrus fruit) to your
drinking water. Doing so will add interest and fresh

taste. In addition to its refreshing, zesty flavor, lemon is an antiseptic and antiscorbutic, meaning that it aids in the prevention of disease and in the cleansing of body impurities.

Water Recipe

Spiced Green Tea for Two

> 2 spiced green tea bags, or 4-6 grams of loose leaf green tea (1-2 tsp. depending on the variety of green tea you are brewing)
>
> 1 kettle cold water
>
> 2 cinnamon sticks
>
> *1-2 tsp. honey

Fill a kettle with cold water and bring to a boil. After removing the kettle from heat, allow it to stand for up to 3 minutes. Pour the heated water over tea bags or loose leaf tea and allow it to steep for up to 3 minutes. If using tea bags, remove the bags. Allow the tea to cool for 3 more minutes. Garnish with cinnamon stick to enhance spicy warm flavor.

* If sweetener is desired, add 1–2 teaspoons of honey.

CUCUMBERS

We remember the fish which we ate freely in Egypt, the cucumbers, the melons.

NUMBERS 11:5

CUCUMBERS IN THE BIBLE

Have you ever noticed that the more fresh fruits and vegetables you eat, the more you want? In Bible times, fresh vegetables were consumed regularly, unlike America today where processed foods filled with additives and hydrogenized fats are the norm. This is a concern of the medical field and should be a concern of ours as well.

How often do you eat whole, fresh foods? In our age of microwave and fast-food eating, some might say they've even forgotten what natural foods taste like.

In his book *What Would Jesus Eat?* Dr. Don Colbert answers the question, Did Jesus eat vegetables?

> Absolutely. We have no direct reference to this, but vegetables were the mainstay of the diet during Bible times. With the exception of the manna-eating years in the wilderness, the Israelites have always eaten a diet loaded with a wide variety of vegetables, herbs, and plant-based species. Numbers 11:5 tells us that the Israelites craved these foods from Egypt: cucumbers, melons, leeks, onions, and garlic, as well as the abundance of fish available to them in Egypt. We should note that these foods were not bad for the Israelites simply because they were Egyptian foods—rather, these were foods that were customarily a part of the Israelites' diet while they lived in Egypt, and they were, therefore, foods they missed as they wandered in the desert wilderness. The fact is, these foods—cucumbers, melons, leeks, onions, and garlic—were very healthy foods, totally approved by God in the dietary laws given to Moses.[1]

Health Benefits of Cucumbers

Fresh cucumbers are an excellent source of many nutrients, including vitamin C, vitamin K, and potassium. Cucumbers also provide dietary fiber, vitamin A, vitamin B_6, thiamine, foliate, pantothenic acid, magnesium, phosphorus, copper, and manganese.

Adding a crisp, crunchy, cool cucumber to your salad is one good way to increase fiber intake. How's that so? The extra fluid you need when increasing fiber occurs naturally in the cucumber. You'll also receive the ever-important beta carotene and folic acid. As a green vegetable, cucumbers also help lower the chances of coronary heart disease. It's best to eat fresh cucumbers, as pickling removes much of the nutrient content, especially vitamin C.

Proper vegetable preparation is key to preserving the maximum nutrients the vegetable offers. Heavily cooked greens lose many of the vitamins and nutrients readily available by eating them raw. Eating greens in a salad, or lightly cooked by steaming, in as small amount of water as possible, will preserve the folic acid, chlorophyll, and plant enzymes present that offer amazing life-giving benefits. A good rule of thumb for vegetable preparation is to look for color intensification. When your vegetables are bright and vivid in color, yet still crisp, they're ready to enjoy.

In *The Gospel of Health,* author Valerie Saxion encourages us to "eat as many fresh fruits and vegetables a day as possible. By eating five daily, according to Johns Hopkins University, you can cut your risk of cancer by 30 percent and lower your systolic blood pressure by 5.5 points and the diastolic pressure by 3.0 points. Their researchers concluded that you could reduce your risk of heart disease by 15 percent and the risk of stroke by 27 percent."[2]

Many people, especially women, turn to the cucumber for a more radiant, glowing complexion. Cucumber juice is a recommended source of silicon. Due to the cucumber's silica components, cucumber juice can have a healthy, connective tissue, effect on the skin.

Cucumbers are also used topically for sunburn. Ascorbic and caffeic acids help prevent water retention, which may be the reason cucumbers help relieve swollen eyes and aid with sunburns. It's a common belief that this vegetable reduces swelling around the eyes. While it is true that cucumbers can reduce swelling, the majority of the cooling effect is from the cucumber's high water makeup.

Organic vegetables grown with natural fertilizers are the best choice. Nutritionalists will tell you that organic green vegetables bring radiant health. No additives, preservatives, food colorings, or artificial flavors are commonly present in organic vegetables that come from a good farmer's field.

Although they may be more expensive and less readily obtained, it's worth going to the extra cost and trouble to provide them to your household. Fruits and vegetables grown organically have no pesticides and contain more vitamins and minerals, such as calcium, iron, and magnesium.

Shopping for organic produce doesn't have to be a chore. Why not turn it into a family outing? Taking your children along with you to a farmer's market is a wonderful opportunity to teach them the importance of selecting and eating natural, whole foods. Good

memories are made in the kitchen and around the dinner table, and your family may find that going to the
market together extends the fun.

As with all vegetables, always remember to wash
cucumbers well before eating them. You may choose a
vegetable wash from the market or just Ivory soap.

Unwaxed cucumbers do not need to be peeled but
should be washed well before cutting. Waxed cucumbers should always be peeled first. Cucumbers can be
sliced, diced, or cut into sticks. While the seeds are
edible and nutritious, some people prefer not to eat
them. To easily remove them, cut the cucumber
lengthwise and use the tip of a spoon to gently scoop
them out.

Cucumber Recipe

Israeli Cucumber Salad
   1-2 large unwaxed cucumbers, thinly sliced
   1 small red onion, thinly sliced
   8-10 red radishes, thinly sliced
   ¼ tsp. salt
   ¼ tsp. lemon pepper
   1 tbsp. chopped chives or parsley

Mix cucumbers, onion, and radishes in a bowl. Season with salt and lemon pepper and mix well. Chill for at least 1 an hour to allow flavors to blend. Garnish with chopped chives or parsley and serve chilled.

Additional Ways to Enjoy Cucumbers

- Use half-inch thick cucumber slices as petite serving "dishes" for chopped-vegetable salads.
- Mix diced cucumbers with sugar snap peas and mint leaves and toss with rice wine vinaigrette.
- For refreshing cold gazpacho soup that takes five minutes or less to make, simply purée cucumbers,

tomatoes, green peppers, and onions, then add salt and pepper to taste.

- Add diced cucumbers to tuna fish or chicken salad recipes.[3]

APPLES

Like an apple tree among the trees of the woods, so is my beloved among the sons. I sat down in his shade with great delight, and his fruit was sweet to my taste.

SONG OF SOLOMON 2:3

APPLES IN THE BIBLE

The sweet, juicy apple renews vigor and brings energy. No wonder it has been eaten for centuries as a source of nourishment as well as a delicious treat. The Bible references fruits such as apples, grapes, pomegranates, figs, berries, melons, apricots, raisins, and dates in numerous places, including Song of Solomon 2:5, which states, *"Sustain me with cakes of raisins, refresh me with apples."*

The forbidden fruit in the Garden of Eden is often referred to as the apple (Genesis 3:3). Through Eve's partaking of the fruit and coaxing Adam to do the same, the apple itself became a representation of temptation. In Latin, the words for "apple" and for "evil" are identical *(malum)*. This may be the reason that the apple was interpreted as the biblical "forbidden fruit." The larynx in the human throat has been called an Adam's apple because of a notion that it was caused by the forbidden fruit sticking in the throat of Adam.

The apple is spoken of in a positive light in the book of Proverbs: *"A word fitly spoken is like apples of gold in settings of silver"* (25:11).

HEALTH BENEFITS OF APPLES

The old saying, "An apple a day keeps the doctor away," has a great deal of medicinal truth to it. The only way, however, to get the maximum nutrition from an apple is to eat the apple raw and unpeeled. Most of the phytonutrients are destroyed by cooking the apples for applesauce or apple juice.

Dr. Don Colbert cites that researchers at Michigan State University have called the apple "the all-around health food." He also provides a list of the many health benefits of this flavorful fruit, citing that apples have been shown to:

- Lower LDL (bad) cholesterol and high blood pressure
- Fight viruses
- Stabilize blood sugar
- Suppress the appetite without robbing the body of necessary nutrients, which is of help especially to those who are attempting to lose weight
- Regulate bowel function, preventing constipation or helping treat diarrhea, depending upon a person's need
- Prevent tooth decay
- Help stop the growth of cancer cells

A person who eats two or three apples a day can greatly boost the body's protection against heart disease. One study conducted in France concluded that a diet heavy in apples actually lowered heart-damaging cholesterol levels from 28 to 52 points, without any other significant changes in eating or exercise habits![1]

Since 1991, the "5 a Day for Better Health" program, a joint project of several large federal agencies and private organizations, has been promoting the idea that we should eat five to nine servings of fruits and vegetables every day. But according to the Centers for Disease Control and *Prevention's* Behavior Risk Factor Surveillance System telephone survey (the world's largest telephone survey), as of 2000, fewer than one in four Americans was actually following this advice, and one in three was consuming only one or two servings every day. That being said, you may wonder what exactly constitutes a serving of a fruits or vegetables? How can you know that you're getting enough of these essential Bible foods? Dr. Reisser shares a list of what constitutes a serving in his book *7 Steps to Healthy Eating:*

- Six ounces (three-quarters of a cup) of fruit or vegetable juice
- One medium-sized whole fruit (such as an orange, apple, or banana)
- One-quarter cup dried fruit

- One-half cup of raw, frozen, or cooked vegetables or fruit (sliced or chopped)
- One cup of raw leafy vegetables. Note that a large salad may contain three cups of greens and thus count as three servings.[2]

Fresh fruits and vegetables are loaded with nutritional benefits, including healthy minerals, vitamins, chlorophyll, and enzymes. In addition, apples help promote good oral health. Added up, this makes apples an excellent overall snack choice for fuel to help keep you going.

Interesting Apple Facts

The top five apple-producing countries in the world are (based on estimate 2004/2005 crop data):

1. China
2. United States
3. Poland
4. Turkey
5. Italy[3]

The top five apple-producing states in the U.S. are:

1. Washington
2. New York
3. Michigan
4. Pennsylvania
5. California[4]

The top fifteen apple varieties grown in the U.S. in 2003, accounting for 90 percent of the total apple production that year include:

1. Red Delicious
2. Golden Delicious
3. Gala
4. Fuji
5. Granny Smith
6. McIntosh
7. Rome
8. Idared
9. Jonathan

10. Empire
11. York
12. Cortland
13. Northern Spy
14. Rhode Island Greening
15. Stayman[5]

More Apple Facts

- Archeologists have found evidence that humans have been enjoying apples since at least 6500 BC.

- The apple tree originated in an area between the Caspian and the Black Sea.

- Apples were introduced to New York by the European settlers who brought seeds with them in the 1600s.

- The apple is the official state fruit of Rhode Island, New York, Washington, and West Virginia. The apple blossom *(pyrus coronaria)* is the official state flower of Arkansas and Michigan.

- Apple varieties range in size from a little larger than a cherry to as large as a grapefruit. There are apples that have an aftertaste of pears, citrus, cinnamon, cloves, coconut, strawberries, grapes, and even pineapple!

- In 2002, the average U.S. consumer ate an estimated 15.8 pounds of fresh-market apples, and 26.4 pounds of processed apples, for a total of 42.2 pounds of fresh apples and processed apple products.

- Sixty percent of the 2002 U.S. apple crop was eaten as fresh fruit, while 39 percent was processed into apple products, and 1 percent was not marketed. Of the 39 percent of the crop that was processed, 18 percent was used in juice and cider; 3 percent was dried; 2 percent was frozen; and 12 percent was canned. Other uses include the making of baby food, apple butter or jelly, and vinegar.

- Apples have five seed pockets or carpels. Each pocket contains seeds. The number of seeds per carpel is determined by the vigor and health of the plant. Different varieties of apples will have different numbers of seeds.

- Planting an apple seed from a particular apple will not produce a tree of that same variety. The seed is a cross of the tree the fruit was grown on and the variety that was the cross pollinator.

- Apples ripen six to ten times faster at room temperature than if they are refrigerated. For optimal storage, apples should be kept at 35–40 degrees with relative humidity of 80–90 percent.

- Apples are a member of the rose family.

- A bushel of apples weighs approximately 42 pounds.

- It takes energy from 50 leaves to produce one apple.

- Fresh apples float because 25 percent of their volume is air.[6]

Apple Recipe

Baked Breakfast Apples

- 2 medium apples
- ½ c. apple juice
- 2 tbsp. raisins and/or pitted whole dates
- 1 tbsp. berry jam, such as strawberry, raspberry, blackberry, or blueberry
- ¼ tsp. ground cinnamon
- ¼ c. low-fat granola cereal
- 1 pinch ground cloves

Chop apples into bite-sized pieces, then combine the apple pieces with the raisins and/or dates in two individual casseroles. Sprinkle the cinnamon and cloves over them. Pour half the apple juice over each apple mixture. Bake covered in 350° F oven about 20 minutes or until apples are slightly tender. Spoon your favorite berry jam on top of the apple mixture and sprinkle with granola. Serve warm. Yields 2 servings.

NUTS

Take some of the best fruits of the land in your vessels and carry down a present for the man—a little balm and a little honey, spices and myrrh, pistachio nuts and almonds.

GENESIS 43:11

NUTS IN THE BIBLE

Second Timothy 1:7 says, *"God hath not given us the spirit of fear; but of power, and of love, and of a sound mind"* (KJV). The Word of God renews our mind in a spiritual sense, but the question arises as to whether God can, through physical means (such as food), also cause changes in the mental realm. He said that He would take sickness away, but His blessing first had to be on our food (Exodus 23:25). Indeed, we have discovered that foods can have a significant effect on mood, memory, and other mental functions.[1] Nuts, a life-giving Bible food, are one of these powerfully beneficial diet choices.

Nuts, such as almonds, pistachios, and walnuts, were plentiful in Jesus's day and were often used as ingredients in desserts. Nuts, we now know, are beneficial in regulating blood sugar and lowering cholesterol when consumed in moderation. Solomon had a "garden of nuts." Many believe this was a grove of walnut trees, since walnuts were highly prized in ancient Israel for the oil they produced. Walnut oil was considered only slightly inferior to olive oil. The walnuts themselves were considered to be a delicious treat. Kings frequently had groves of almond, walnut, and pistachio trees along with their olive and fig tree groves. Walnuts were so highly prized that they were called the "royal" nut.[2]

For centuries in Israel, nuts have been a gift that signifies peace and goodwill. *Kibbet*, which means "treat" in Hebrew, is a mixture of dates, figs, raisins, and nuts. It is often offered to visitors or is served at the end of a meal with honey, yogurt, and tea. A very common dish served at the Passover meal is *haroset,* a dish that symbolizes the mortar that the Hebrew slaves used in building Pharaoh's pyramids. Haroset is made by combining three-fourths cup of chopped almonds, walnuts, or other nuts with three cups of chopped apples, a half cup of raisins, a half cup of chopped dates, a half teaspoon of cinnamon, and three-fourths cup of grape juice or red wine.[3]

HEALTH BENEFITS OF NUTS

Nuts are a delicious addition to many of the world's finest cuisines. They add an array of flavors and textures, making ordinary dishes delightful. Tree nuts, in particular, offer an array of health benefits. Tree nuts include almonds, Brazils, cashews, hazelnuts, macadamias, pecans, pine nuts, pistachios, and walnuts. Important nutrients found in these nuts are fiber, vitamins such as niacin, folic acid, and vitamins E and B_6, and minerals such as magnesium, potassium, phosphorus, selenium, and zinc.

According to the USDA, some nuts and seeds (flax, walnuts) are excellent sources of essential fatty acids, and some (sunflower seeds, almonds, hazelnuts) are good sources of vitamin E, which supports the circulatory system and protects the heart. A lack of vitamin E can lead to damage of the red blood cells, nervous system, eyes, heart, arteries, and cause poor coordination. Nuts are also high in selenium, which helps elevate mood. Nuts are a good source of protein and may help protect against heart disease, cancer, and other chronic diseases. Almonds, hempseed, sunflower seeds, and pumpkin seeds are beneficial as well.

It's more nutritious to eat nuts raw. They're a wonderful treat to serve to your family as a snack food. Peanuts are less nutritious and are classified as a legume rather than a nut. They are high in fungus and may cause allergic reactions in children. And steer clear of nuts that contain added salt and sugar.

Nuts are considered a "power food" and make an excellent treat to add to your daily diet. They are naturally rich in zinc, copper, iron, calcium, magnesium, and phosphorus. Top healthcare professionals agree that nuts are among the top cancer-fighting foods in the world. Not only do they serve to stabilize blood sugar levels, but they also help you to avoid other less nutritious snacks that may have sugar or unneeded carbohydrates. Nutrition experts recommend a handful of nuts a day—roughly fifteen to twenty cashews.

Adding one ounce of nuts and seeds to your diet increases your protein intake by eight grams, about as much as a glass of milk.

If you're concerned about the fat in nuts being bad, don't be. They contain monounsaturated fats, considered good fats. Genesis 43:11 specifically mentions pistachios and almonds, both of which are known to be lower in fat and calories.

NUTS RECIPE

Banana Nut Bread

   1½ c. all-purpose flour

   ½ c. sugar

   2½ tsp. baking powder

   ½ tsp. salt

   ½ tsp. baking soda

   1 c. wheat squares, cereal crushed to ½ c.

   ⅔ c. chopped nuts

   1 egg, slightly beaten

   ¼ c. vegetable oil

   2 tbsp. water

   1½ c. mashed bananas, or 3 large bananas

   1 tsp. vanilla

Preheat oven to 350° F. Grease an 81½ x 41½ x 21½ inch loaf pan. Stir together flour, sugar, baking powder, salt, baking soda, wheat squares cereal, and nuts. Combine egg, oil, water, mashed bananas, and vanilla. Add all at once to dry ingredients. Stir just until moistened. Spread evenly into the pan. Bake 50–55 minutes or until tester inserted in center comes out clean. Let cool 15 minutes before removing from pan. Makes one loaf.

CREATIVE WAYS TO EAT NUTS

In addition to eating a handful of nuts each day, here are some foods you might enjoy sprinkling nuts on:

- Salads
- Yogurt
- Cereal
- Pasta
- Cooked vegetables
- Muffins and pancakes (toss a handful or two into your batter)

Eating God's Way

Beloved, I pray that you may prosper in all things and be in health, just as your soul prospers.

3 John 2

Back to the Bible

God has given us wisdom to make the best choices as it relates to dietary considerations. As we get back to the basics of the Bible we'll find a wealth of nutrition for our spiritual as well as our physical beings. The Lord desires to flow through vessels of honor that are strong and prepared to do His good work on the earth today.

But in a great house there are not only vessels of gold and silver, but also of wood and clay, some for honor and some for dishonor. Therefore if anyone cleanses himself from the latter, he will be a vessel for honor, sanctified and useful for the Master, prepared for every good work. (2 Timothy 2:20-21)

For this reason we also, since the day we heard it, do not cease to pray for you, and to ask that you may be filled with the knowledge of His will in all wisdom and spiritual understanding; that you may walk worthy of the Lord, fully pleasing Him, being fruitful in every good work and increasing in the knowledge of God; strengthened with all might, according to His glorious power, for all patience and longsuffering with joy; giving thanks to the Father who has qualified us to be partakers of the inheritance of the saints in the light. He has delivered us from the power of darkness and conveyed us into the kingdom of the Son of His love, in whom we have redemption through His blood, the forgiveness of sins. (Colossians 1:9-14)

THE COMING MOVE OF GOD AND YOU

The Lord, mighty in heaven and earth, created you to thrive, not just survive. You are His child, qualified, delivered, adopted, and redeemed into an everlasting kingdom. The heavenly fold in all its fullness is yours. Now is the time to rise up and equip yourself through prayer, fasting, daily Bible reading, and fellowship with other believers.

Why is this urgent? The last days' move of God is at hand, and God is looking for prepared vessels that He can flow freely through. How exciting it is that the day is here when His magnificent presence, power, and glory shine abroad. This is the day of salvation, deliverance, and healing.

Standing as a strong Christian soldier, both spiritually and physically, is essential; for as you stand healthy in Christ you're able to fight the enemy's darkness and see those entangled in the prison of death delivered and set free.

What does this have to do with Bible foods for life? Proper nourishment is vital to your physical body. It plays a key role in your overall preparation for victorious Christian living as an active and alert soldier in God's kingdom: *"You therefore must endure hardship as a good soldier of Jesus Christ. No one engaged in warfare entangles himself with the affairs of this life, that he may please him who enlisted him as a soldier"* (2 Timothy 2:3-4).

God in heaven, who is our commanding King (see Psalm 44:4-8), has enlisted you in His great army. Therefore, He is counting on you be faithful. When you gave your life to the Lord Jesus, the day you were saved and born again, you gave Him all of you. *All* means holding nothing back.

The Power That Keeps You

God knows we are not perfect, and He knows the struggles we face. Yet, by His mighty Spirit, there is great power to keep us each and every day. David understood this mighty spiritual principle as he prayed: *"Keep my soul, and deliver me; let me not be ashamed, for I put my trust in You. Let integrity and uprightness preserve me, for I wait for You"* (Psalm 25:20-21).

No matter what your health needs are, be encouraged today—God cares for you. You can give your whole self to Him again, and ask Him to help you with the areas where you struggle.

This may be with your diet, possibly eating junk food that contains empty calories. Or maybe it's your lack of exercise, complacency with a sedentary lifestyle. Or perhaps you're not getting enough sleep at night. God can help you—and He will, if you just ask Him.

You were created in the Lord's image. He knows you entirely and loves you through and through. You are accepted in Christ just the way you are. No matter what health or physical difficulties you might be facing today, God is bigger than all your cares.

THIS IS YOUR DAY FOR A BREAKTHROUGH!

Today is your day for a breakthrough. Just as surely as you call upon the Lord Jesus, He is there, ever present to minister great health and life to you. Psalm 86:7 declares: *"In the day of my trouble I will call upon You, for You will answer me."*

Every detail that affects your healthy life is important to Him, including your physical, mental, emotional, and spiritual wellness. With God at your side, nothing is too hard. The prophet Jeremiah understood this, as he proclaimed: *"Ah, Lord GOD! Behold, You have made the heavens and the earth by Your great power and outstretched arm. There is nothing too hard for You"* (Jeremiah 32:17).

Won't you trust in God with all your heart today? As you take His hand, He has promised to lead and guide you into a healthy place, a place of proliferate blessing and flourishing life:

> *Grace and peace be multiplied to you in the knowledge of God and of Jesus our Lord, as His divine power has given to us all things that pertain to life and godliness, through the knowledge of Him who called us by glory and virtue, by which have been given to us exceedingly great and precious promises.* (2 Peter 1:2-4)

Never forget, He is your Creator (see Psalm 139:15). You can confidently yield your whole life in His loving hands. He'll never let you down. Make a lasting decision to stand strong and healthy in God's precious Word.

Remember the wonderful Lord Jesus is coming again soon. Until then, may you experience renewed vigor and plentiful health, eating God's way, with marvelous Bible foods for life today!

ADDITIONAL HEALTHY FOODS: EZEKIEL BREAD, TOMATOES, AND YOGURT

*For the Lord your God is bringing you into a good land
. . . a land of wheat . . . in which you will lack nothing.*

DEUTERONOMY 8:7–9

A s an added bonus, here are a few extra foods that provide marvelous life-giving substance. These foods supply health and infuse nourishment when eaten regularly: Ezekiel bread, tomatoes, and yogurt.

EZEKIEL BREAD

The text of the Old Testament book Ezekiel contains a tremendous Bible food recipe for life:

Take for yourself wheat, barley, beans, lentils, millet, and spelt; put them into one vessel, and make bread of them for yourself. (Ezekiel 4:9)

According to Dr. Reginald Cherry's *The Bible Cure*, each specific food contained in the bread mentioned in Ezekiel 4:9 has particular benefits for our health and for preventing disease.

Here are a few of the scientific findings Dr. Cherry listed relating to these food items:

Wheat and spelt lower risk for heart disease. Be sure you use whole wheat, including the bran and germ—not refined wheat. Whole wheat is an excellent source of B complex vitamins, phosphorus, iron, and vitamin E. The vitamin E in wheat helps the body reduce the production of free radicals (which cause LDL cholesterol to stick to artery walls), thus reducing the risk of heart disease. The fiber in wheat helps to reduce the risk of colon cancer.

Barley also helps to lower your risk of heart disease. Do your arteries a favor by eating both wheat and barley. Barley can help lower cholesterol, reduce the formation of blood clots, improve digestion, and reduce the risk of certain forms of cancer. It fights heart disease in two ways: The tocopherols in barley help to stop free radical oxidation, a process that makes LDL cholesterol (the dangerous type) stick to artery walls. They also help to prevent tiny blood clots from forming. Because barley is high in selenium and vitamin E, it helps protect and fight against cancer.

Beans (pinto, lentils, kidney, great northern, and others) help lower cholesterol and are packed with soluble fiber. They can also help to stabilize blood sugar levels, reduce the risk of breast and prostate cancers, and lower the risk of heart disease in people with diabetes.

Millet and spelt can help to ease premenstrual discomfort and to speed healing in wounds. Millet contains protein, which helps the body build and repair muscles, connective fibers, and other tissues.[1]

EZEKIEL BREAD RECIPE

Ezekiel Bread (Adapted from Ezekiel 4:9)

2½ c. whole wheat

1⅔ c. whole rye

½ c. barley

¼ c. millet

¼ c. lentils

2 tbsp. great northern beans, uncooked

2 tbsp. red kidney beans, uncooked

2 tbsp. pinto beans, uncooked

2 c. lukewarm water, divided

½ c. plus 1 tsp. honey, divided

2 tbsp. yeast

¼ c. extra-virgin olive oil

Measure and combine all the above ingredients in a large bowl. Put this mixture into a flour mill and grind. The flour should be the consistency of regular flour. Coarse flour may cause digestion problems. This makes 8 cups of flour. Use 4 cups per batch of bread. Measure 4 cups of flour into a large bowl. Store the remaining flour mixture for future use. Measure 1 cup lukewarm water (110–115°) in a small mixing bowl. Add 1 teaspoon of the honey and the yeast, stir to dissolve the yeast, cover, and set aside, allowing the yeast to rise for 5–10 minutes. In a small mixing bowl, combine the following: olive oil, ½ cup honey, and the remaining cup of warm water. Mix well then add this to the flour mixture in the large bowl. Add the yeast to the bowl and stir until well mixed. The mixture should be the consistency of slightly "heavy" cornbread. Spread the mixture evenly in an 11" x 15" pan sprayed with no-cholesterol cooking oil. Let the mixture rise for one hour in a warm place. Bake at 375° F for approximately 30 minutes. Check for doneness. Bread should be the consistency of baked cornbread.[2]

TOMATOES

Tomatoes not only are delicious, but health experts tell us they contain three phytonutrients that help prevent the formation of cancer cells. When eaten regularly, lycopene, a red pigment in the tomato, is an antioxidant that may help prevent some types of cancer. Sliced tomatoes and tomato juice are nutritious choices for your good health. Cooked tomatoes are even better for you, so feel free to add ketchup to your other foods.

Tomato Recipe

Greek Stuffed Tomatoes

   2 tbsp. olive oil

   1 c. onion, chopped

   2 c. fresh spinach, chopped

   2 tsp. dried basil

   ½ c. bread crumbs

   1 egg

   ½ lb. feta cheese, crumbled

   salt, to taste

   pepper, to taste

   6 tomatoes, firm and with insides scooped out

Heat oil in a saucepan over medium heat, and sauté onion until translucent. Add spinach and cook for two minutes. In a bowl, combine the onion and spinach mixture with all remaining ingredients except tomatoes. Stuff filling into tomatoes and bake in a preheated, 350° F oven for 15 minutes. Serves 6.

Yogurt

Many leading nutritionists claim that yogurt, or fermented milk, is a super food and among the healthiest of the dairy choices due to the lactobacillus acidophilus and other friendly bacteria, as well as the vitamins A and B it contains. Yogurt is high in calcium and good for building bone mass. Some specialists say it has been linked to the prevention of colds, allergies, cancer, and dangerous intestinal infections.

Yogurt is a natural antibiotic. The live cultures help fight infection. It keeps the digestive system and intestinal track healthy and aids in healthy bowel function. If you are looking for a good food to help balance the immune system—yogurt is a winner. Experts say yogurt has aided in the health and vitality of many civilizations.

Nonfat, plain yogurt is the best choice. Yogurt with added sugar, fruit, artificial flavors, sweeteners, or color is less desirable. To enhance the flavor of plain yogurt, try adding your own favorite fruits, granola, or nuts. Remember to select yogurt that contains live cultures of bacteria.

Yogurt Recipe

Honey Yogurt Fruit Dip

    4 c. fruit, see suggestions*

    1 c. low-fat plain yogurt

    1 tbsp. almonds, toasted slices or slivers

    1 tsp. grated orange rind

    2 tbsp. honey

    ½ tsp. vanilla or almond extract

Mix sauce ingredients in a bowl. Cover and refrigerate for 1 hour. Spoon onto fresh fruit or serve as dip.

*Suggested fruit:

- Sliced oranges, bananas, kiwi, pineapple, cantaloupe or honeydew
- Strawberries, raspberries, blackberries, blueberries, grapes
- Combinations: grapes and melon, melon and blueberries, blackberries and sliced peaches, raspberries and blueberries, strawberries and kiwi, bananas and kiwi, bananas and sliced oranges

Popular Middle Eastern Yogurt Recipe

A very popular salad in the Middle East is yogurt based. To 2 cups of plain yogurt, add 2 tablespoons minced fresh mint (or 2 teaspoons dried mint), two cloves of crushed garlic, and 2 large cucumbers (sliced). The yogurt mixture is sometimes served on a bed of watercress and sliced radishes.[2]

NOTES

Fish

    1. Don Colbert, *What Would Jesus Eat?* (Nashville: Thomas Nelson, 2002), 36.

    2. Jordan Rubin, *The Maker's Diet* (Lake Mary, FL: Siloam, 2005), 145.

    3. Don Colbert, *Walking in Divine Health* (Lake Mary, FL: Siloam, 1999), 114.

Beans

    1. Colbert, *What Would Jesus Eat?* 84–85.

    2. Colbert, *What Would Jesus Eat?* 87–88.

Leeks, Onions, and Garlic

    1. Colbert, *What Would Jesus Eat?* 90.

    2. Reese Dubin, *Miracle Food Cures from the Bible* (Paramus, NJ: Prentice Hall, 1999), 321.

Water

    1. K. C. Craichy, *Super Health: 7 Golden Keys to Unlock Lifelong Vitality* (Minneapolis: Bronze Bow Publishing, 2005), 13.

    2. Craichy, *Super Health*, 15.

    3. Colbert, *What You Don't Know May Be Killing You!* (Lake Mary: FL: Siloam, 2004), 27.

Cucumbers

    1. Colbert, *What Would Jesus Eat?* 82.

    2. Valerie Saxion, *The Gospel of Health* (Minneapolis: Bronze Bow Publishing, 2004), 138.

3. The World's Healthiest Foods, "Cucumber." Found at www.whfoods.com on 26 August 2006.

Apples

1. Colbert, *What Would Jesus Eat?* 154.
2. Paul C. Reisser, *7 Steps to Healthy Eating* (Carol Stream, IL: Tyndale) 27–28.
3. USDA Foreign Agricultural Service: Production, Supply, and Distribution, "World Apple Production Since 1996." Found at www.fas.usda.gov/psd on 14 August 2006.
4. All About Apples, "Apple Facts." Found at www.allabout apples.com/facts on 14 August 2006.
5. All About Apples.
6. All About Apples.

Nuts

1. Reginald Cherry, *The Bible Cure* (Lake Mary, FL: Creation House, 1998), 98.
2. Colbert, *What Would Jesus Eat?* 161–62.
3. Colbert, *What Would Jesus Eat?* 163.

Additional Healthy Foods

1. Cherry, *The Bible Cure,* 89.
2. Cherry, *The Bible Cure,* 90–91.
3. Recipe Source, "Greek Stuffed Tomatoes." Found at www.recipesource.com on 26 August 2006.

Yogurt

1. Recipe Source, "Berries with Orange-Honey Yogurt," adapted.
2. Colbert, *What Would Jesus Eat?* 77.